DADDY

BY
RUPERT FAWCETT

BOXTREE

First published 1996 by Boxtree
an imprint of Macmillan Publishers Ltd
25 Eccleston Place, London SW1W 9NF
and Basingstoke

Associated companies throughout the world

ISBN: 0 7522 2280 5

9 8 7 6 5 4

A CIP catalogue record for this book is available from the British Library.

Printed and bound in Great Britain by Redwood Books, Trowbridge, Wiltshire

**A full range of DADDY greetings cards is available from
Paperlink Ltd. Tel: 0171 582 8244**

Not being content with the huge success of his cartoon character, Fred, whose greeting cards continue to sell in millions, Rupert Fawcett has come up with another brilliant creation in DADDY.

This new collection contains 60 cartoons following the trials and tribulations of the hapless DADDY as he struggles to come to terms with the realities of parenthood.

Rupert was born and brought up in West London where he still lives with his wife and (surprise, surprise) two small children. Included in his various other projects is a follow-up to this long-awaited collection.

1.

2.

5.

6.

3.

4.

7.

8.

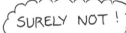

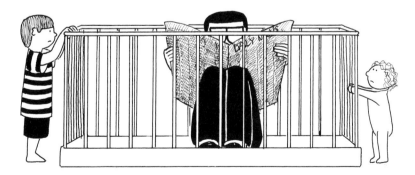

1. *I CAN'T BELIEVE I'M ACTUALLY GOING TO RING ONE OF THESE TELEPHONE SERVICES*

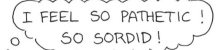

2. *I FEEL SO PATHETIC! SO SORDID!*

5. *THE ENDLESS BILLS! THE MORTGAGE! THE HUGE OVERDRAFT! THE SARCASTIC BANK MANAGER!*

6. *THE HARD-TO-PLEASE BOSS! THE DEMANDING CHILDREN! THE PERMANENTLY EXHAUSTED WIFE!*

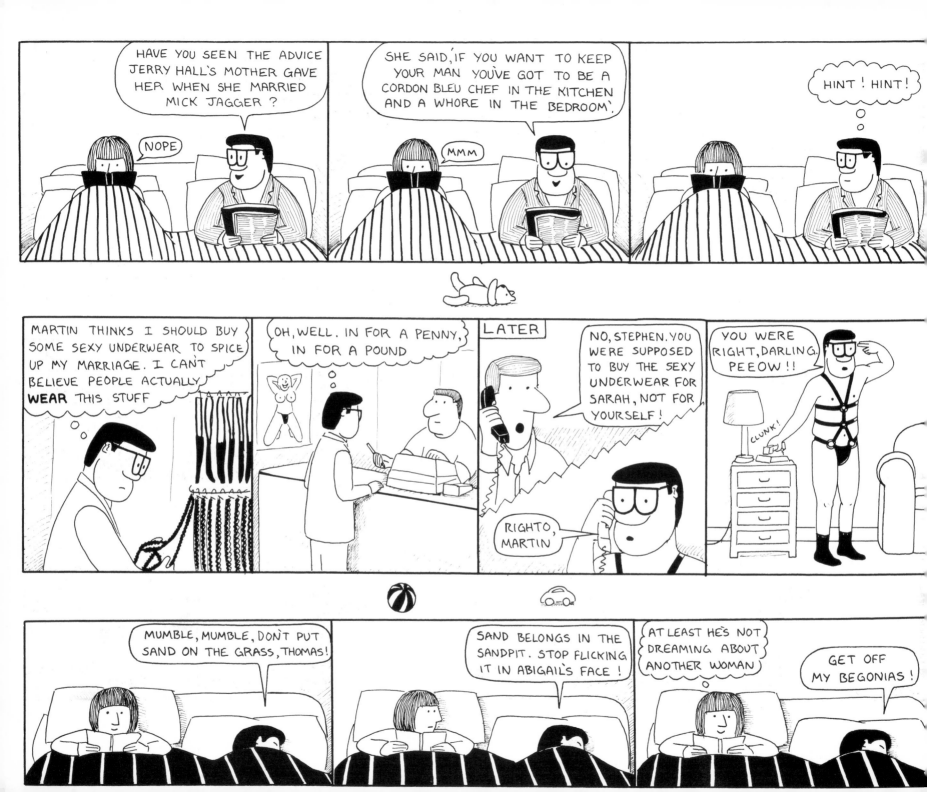